Favorite Christmas Carols

CONTENTS

ACKNOWLEDGMENT

*Copyright 1948 by the Hall & McCreary Company. Copyright renewed
1976 by Schmitt Publications, 110 North Fifth Street, Minneapolis,
Minnesota 55403. All rights reserved. Used by permission.*

ISBN 0-89542-474-6 150
COPYRIGHT © 1978 BY IDEALS PUBLISHING CORPORATION
MILWAUKEE, WIS. 53201
ALL RIGHTS RESERVED. PRINTED AND BOUND IN U.S.A.

Editorial Director, James Kuse
Managing Editor, Ralph Luedtke
Photographic Editor, Gerald Koser
Production Editor, Stuart L. Zyduck

O Little Town of Bethlehem

PHILLIPS BROOKS

**AMERICAN
LEWIS H. REDNER**

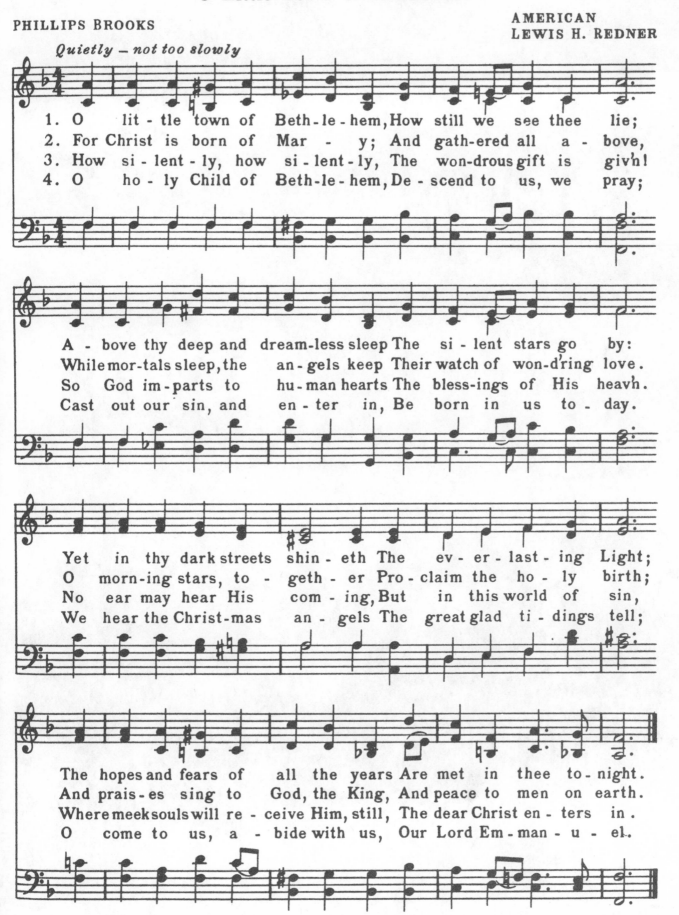

It Came upon the Midnight Clear

EDWIN H. SEARS

AMERICAN
RICHARD S. WILLIS

With quiet joy

1. It came up-on—the mid-night clear, That glo-ri-ous song of old,——
2. Still thro' the clo-ven skies they come, With peace-ful wings un-furled;——
3. For lo! the days are has-t'ning on, By proph-ets seen of old,——

From an-gels bend-ing near the earth, To touch their harps of gold:——
And still their heav'n-ly mu-sic floats O'er all the wea-ry world.——
When with the ev-er-cir-cling years Shall come the time fore-told,——

"Peace on the earth, good will to men From heav'n's all gra-cious King;"
A-bove its sad and low-ly plains They bend on hov'r-ing wing,
When the new heav'n and earth shall own The Prince of Peace their King,

The world in sol-emn still-ness lay To hear the an-gels sing.——
And ev-er o'er its Ba-bel sounds The bless-ed an-gels sing.——
And the whole world send back the song Which now the an-gels sing.——

Away in a Manger

MARTIN LUTHER

GERMAN
Arranged by R. H.

The First Noel

TRADITIONAL

FRENCH

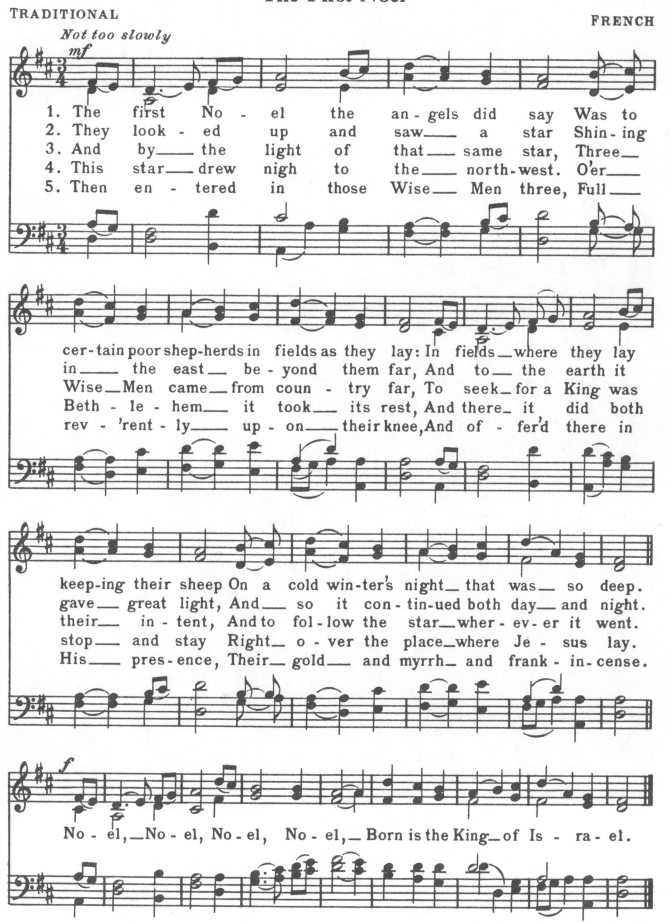

O Come, All Ye Faithful

Adeste Fideles

LATIN HYMN
Translated by FREDERICK OAKELEY

WADE'S CANTUS DIVERSI

With joyful majesty

1. { O come, all ye faith-ful, Joy-ful and tri-umph-ant, O
   { Ad-es-te fi-de-les, Lae-ti tri-umph-ant-es; Ve

2. { — Sing choirs of an-gels, Sing in ex-ul-ta-tion, —
   { — Can-tet nunc I-o! Cho-rus an-ge-lo-rum; —

come ye, O come ye to Beth-le-hem. Come and be-
ni-te, ve-ni-te in Beth-le-hem; Na-tum vi-
Sing all ye cit-i-zens of heav'n — a-bove: Glo-ry to
Can-tet nunc au-la coe-le-sti-um; Glo-ri-a,

hold Him, Born the King of An-gels: O come, let us a-dore Him, O
de-te, Re-gem an-ge-lo-rum: Ve-ni-te a-do-re-mus, Ve-
God — In the high-est, glo-ry! O come, let us a-dore Him, O
Glo-ri-a In ex-cel-sis De-o! Ve-ni-te a-do-re-mus, Ve-

come, let us a-dore Him, O come, let us a-dore Him, Christ the Lord.
ni-te, a-do-re-mus, Ve-ni-te, a-do-re-mus Do-mi-num.

3. Yea, Lord we greet Thee, Born this happy morning.
Jesus, to Thee be all glory giv'n.
Word of the Father, now in flesh appearing.

3. *Ergo qui natus die hodierna,*
Jesu, tibi sit gloria,
Patris aeterni Verbum caro factum:

Joy to the World

ISAAC WATTS

GEORGE F. HÄNDEL
Arranged by Lowell Mason

We Three Kings of Orient Are

J.H.H. JR.

AMERICAN
JOHN H. HOPKINS JR.

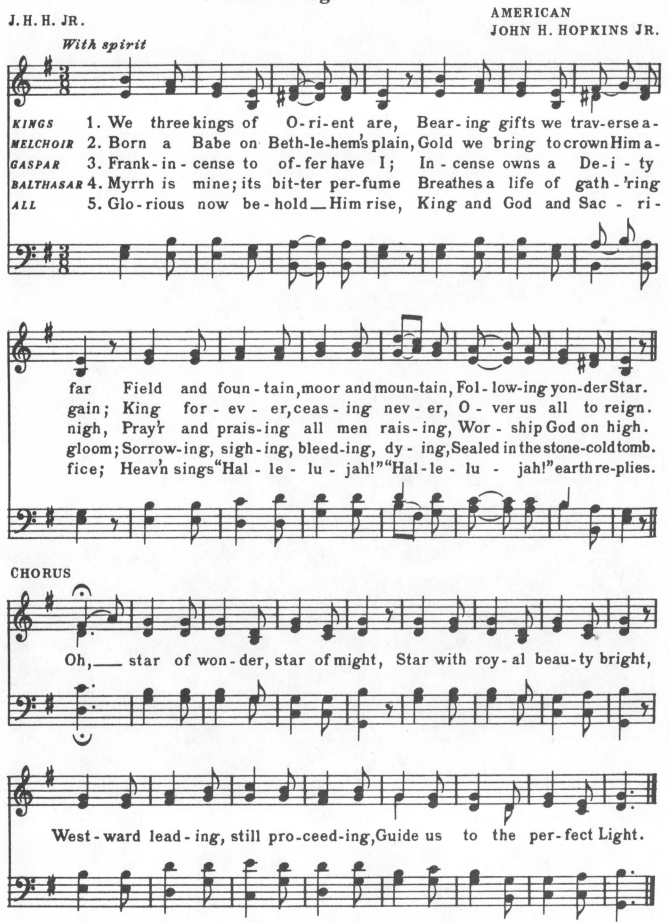

O Christmas Tree
O Tannenbaum

Translated from the German
English version by RUTH HELLER

GERMAN

Happily

1. O Christ-mas tree, O Christ-mas tree, O tree of green, un-chang-ing. Your boughs, so green in sum-mer time, Do brave the snow of win-ter-time. O Christ-mas tree, O Christ-mas tree, O tree of green, un-chang-ing.

2. O Christ-mas tree, O Christ-mas tree, You set my heart a-sing-ing. Like lit-tle stars, your can-dles bright Send to the world a won-drous light. O Christ-mas tree, O Christ-mas tree, You set my heart a-sing-ing.

3. O Christ-mas tree, O Christ-mas tree, You come from God, e-ter-nal. A sym-bol of the Lord of Love Whom God to man sent from a-bove. O Christ-mas tree, O Christ-mas tree, You come from God, e-ter-nal.

4. O Christ-mas tree, O Christ-mas tree, You speak of God, un-chang-ing. You tell us all to faith-ful be, And trust in God e-ter-nal-ly. O Christ-mas tree, O Christ-mas tree, You speak of God, un-chang-ing.

Hark! the Herald Angels Sing

CHARLES WESLEY

ENGLISH
FELIX MENDELSSOHN
Arr. by W. H. Cummings

Joyfully

1. Hark! the her - ald an - gels sing, "Glo - ry to the new-born King!
2. Christ, by high - est heav'n a - dored; Christ, the ev - er - last-ing Lord;
3. Hail! the heav'n-born Prince of Peace! Hail! the Son of Right-eous-ness!

Peace on earth, and mer-cy mild, God and sin-ners rec-on-ciled."
Late in time be - hold Him come, Off-spring of the fa-vored one.
Light and life to all He brings, Ris'n with heal-ing in His wings.

Joy - ful, all ye na-tions, rise, Join the tri-umph of the skies;
Veiled in flesh, the God-head see; Hail th'in-car-nate De - i - ty
Mild He lays His glo - ry by, Born that man no more may die:

With th'an-gel - ic host pro-claim, "Christ is born in Beth-le-hem."
Pleased, as man with men to dwell, Je - sus our Im-man-u - el!
Born to raise the sons of earth, Born to give them sec-ond birth.

Hark! the her - ald an-gels sing, "Glo - ry to the new-born King!"

Angels We Have Heard on High

TRADITIONAL   FRENCH

Joyously

1. An - gels we have heard on high, Sweet-ly sing-ing o'er the plains;
2. Shep-herds, why this ju - bi - lee? Why your joy-ous songs pro-long?
3. Come to Beth - le - hem and see Him whose birth the an-gels sing;

And the moun - tains in re - ply Ech - o - ing their joy - ous strains.
What the glad - some ti - dings be Which in - spire your heav'n-ly song?
Come a - dore on bend - ed knee Christ, the Lord, our new-born King.

Glo - - - - - ri - a

in ex - cel - sis De - o, Glo -

- - - ri - a in ex-cel-sis De - o!

What Child Is This?

WILLIAM C. DIX

Moderately

ENGLISH
Arranged by Sir John Stainer

1. What Child is this, Who laid to rest On Mar - y's lap is sleep-ing? Whom an-gels greet with an-thems sweet, While shep-herds watch are keep-ing?
2. Why lies He in such mean es-tate, Where ox and ass are feed-ing? Good Chris-tian, fear: for sin-ners here The si - lent Word is plead-ing;
3. So bring Him in - cense, gold, and myrrh, Come peas-ant, king to own Him; The King of kings sal - va-tion brings; Let lov - ing hearts en-throne Him.

This, this is Christ, the King; Whom shep-herds guard and an - gels sing:
Nails, spear shall pierce Him through, The Cross be born for me, for you;
Raise, raise the song on high, The Vir - gin sings her lul - la - by;

Haste, haste to bring Him laud, The Babe, the Son of Mar - y!
Hail, hail the Word made flesh, The Babe, the Son of Mar - y!
Joy, joy for Christ is born, The Babe, the Son of Mar - y!

Silent Night

Stille Nacht, Heilige Nacht

JOSEPH MÖHR

GERMAN
FRANZ GRÜBER

1. Si - lent night! Ho - ly night! All is calm, all is bright.
2. Si - lent night! Ho - ly night! Shep-herds quake at the sight!
3. Si - lent night! Ho - ly night! Son of God, love's pure light!

Round yon Vir - gin Moth-er and Child! Ho - ly In-fant, so ten-der and mild,
Glo - ries stream from heav-en a - far, Heav'n-ly hosts sing, "Al - le - lu - ia!"
Ra - diant beams from Thy ho - ly face With the dawn of re - deem - ing grace,

Sleep in heav - en - ly peace!__ Sleep in heav - en - ly peace!__
Christ, the Sav - ior, is born!__ Christ, the Sav - ior, is born!__
Je - sus, Lord, at Thy birth!__ Je - sus, Lord, at Thy birth!__

God Rest You Merry, Gentlemen

TRADITIONAL

ENGLISH
Arranged by Sir John Stainer

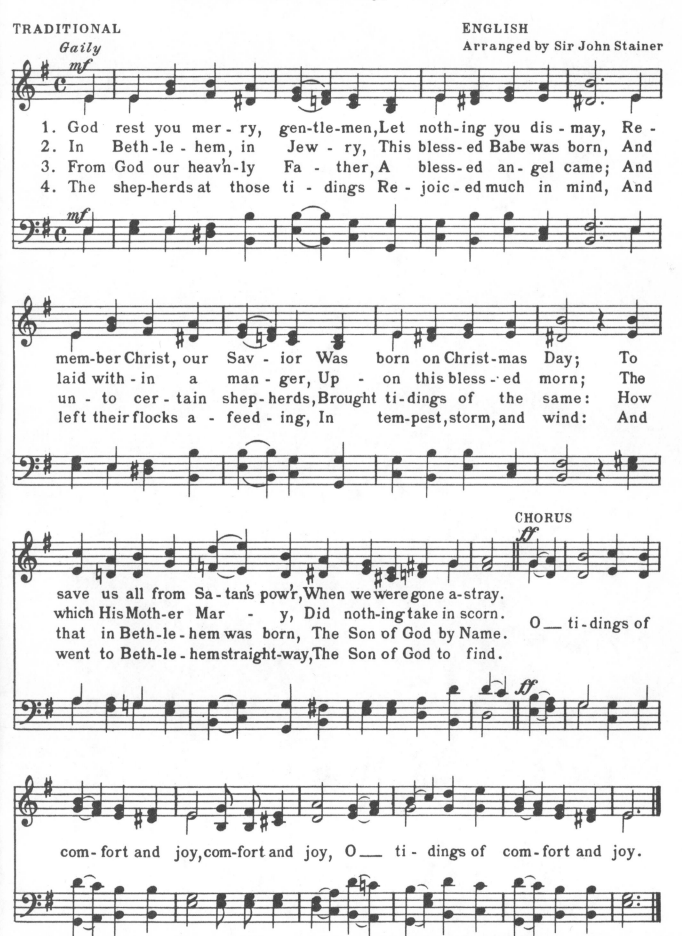

1. God rest you mer - ry, gen-tle-men, Let noth-ing you dis - may, Re -
2. In Beth-le-hem, in Jew - ry, This bless-ed Babe was born, And
3. From God our heav'n-ly Fa - ther, A bless-ed an - gel came; And
4. The shep-herds at those ti - dings Re - joic-ed much in mind, And

mem-ber Christ, our Sav - ior Was born on Christ-mas Day; To
laid with-in a man - ger, Up - on this bless-ed morn; The
un - to cer - tain shep-herds, Brought ti-dings of the same: How
left their flocks a - feed - ing, In tem-pest, storm, and wind: And

CHORUS

save us all from Sa-tan's pow'r, When we were gone a-stray.
which His Moth-er Mar - y, Did noth-ing take in scorn.
that in Beth-le-hem was born, The Son of God by Name. O — ti-dings of
went to Beth-le-hem straight-way, The Son of God to find.

com-fort and joy, com-fort and joy, O — ti - dings of com-fort and joy.

Deck the Hall

TRADITIONAL WELSH

Rollicking

1. Deck the hall with boughs of hol - ly, Fa la la la la, la la la la.
2. See the blaz - ing Yule be - fore us, Fa la la la la, la la la la.
3. Fast a - way the old year pass - es, Fa la la la la, la la la la.

'Tis the sea - son to be jol - ly, Fa la la la la, la la la la.
Strike the harp and join the cho - rus, Fa la la la la, la la la la.
Hail the new, ye lads and lass - es, Fa la la la la, la la la la.

Don we now our gay ap - par - el, Fa la, la la, la la la,
Fol - low me in mer - ry meas - ure, Fa la, la la, la la la,
Sing we joy - ous all to - geth - er, Fa la, la la, la la la,

Troll the an - cient Yule - tide car - ol, Fa la la la la, la la la la.
While I tell of Yule - tide treas - ure, Fa la la la la, la la la la.
Heed - less of the wind and weath - er, Fa la la la la, la la la la.

Jolly Old Saint Nicholas

1. Jol - ly old Saint Ni - cho - las, Lean your ear this way! Don't you tell a
2. When the clock is strik - ing twelve, When I'm fast a - sleep, Down the chim - ney
3. John - ny wants a pair of skates; Su - sy wants a sled; Nel - lie wants a

sin - gle soul What I'm going to say;___ Christ - mas Eve is com - ing soon;
broad and black, With your pack you'll creep;___ All the stock - ings you will find
pic - ture book; Yel - low, blue and red;___ Now I think I'll leave to you

Now, you dear old man, Whis - per what you'll bring to me; Tell me if you can.
Hang - ing in a row; Mine will be the short - est one, You'll be sure to know.
What to give the rest; Choose for me, dear San - ta Claus, You will know the best.